Shingi Itoh

The White Egret

BRAMBLES © Gay Corran 1986

This Book
Belongs to

Liza

BLANDFORD

First published in the United Kingdom 1989 by Blandford Press
An imprint of Cassell Plc
Artillery House, Artillery Row, London SWIP 1RT

First published in the United States 1988 by Chronicle Books,
275 Fifth Street, San Francisco, California 94103.

Distributed in Australia by
Capricorn Link (Australia) Pty Ltd
PO Box 665, Lane Cove, NSW 2066

British Library Cataloging in Publication Data

Itoh, Shingi, 1920–
    The white egret
    1. Egrets
    I. Title
    598.34

    ISBN 0-7137-2137-5

Editing: Deborah Stone
Cover design: Karen Pike
English translation: Lori Nakaoka

Printed in Japan
First published by Yama To Keikoku Sha, Tokyo, Japan

10 9 8 7 6 5 4 3 2 1

A fledgling practices flapping its wings.

Contents

3 *During the mating season the lores of the great egret turn bluish green and for a short period the irises turn red.*

4 *During the mating season the lores of the intermediate egret remain yellow and the irises become bright red.*

5 *The lores of the little egret turn from reddish purple to crimson. The bill stays black throughout the year.*

6 *Breeding plumage of the great egret.*

7 *Breeding plumage of the intermediate egret.*

8 *Long head feathers and curled breeding plumage are distinctive features of the little egret.*

Foreword

No one turning the pages of this outstanding photographic portfolio of white egrets can fail to be moved by the elegant beauty of these glamorous birds who grace the waterways of our lands. In the avian world the grace and charm of the heron family have long held high profile. When the plume hunters ravaged the great heron colonies to provide trimmings for ladies' hats to the fashion houses of London, Paris, and New York, huge numbers were killed in pursuit of their fragile plumes. Such unrestrained savagery led to the creation of the conservation movements of today.

In Japan, the heronries, protected since the time of the shoguns, have now received support from the Wild Bird Society. The sheer glamour of white egrets, which so nearly led to their complete demise, has now been recognized and their future is hopefully no longer under such dire threat. Dr. Shingi Itoh has enhanced the chances of their survival with this timely book. His portrayal of the white egrets of Japan is superb; each photograph is a masterpiece. Dr. Itoh has captured, with quite astonishing artistic skill, the graceful movements and varying habits of these birds. His collection will appeal not only to bird lovers, but to amateur and professional photographers alike, who will recognize his unique combination of photographic skill and deep understanding of and sympathy with his subject.

James Hancock
Coauthor of *The Herons of the World*,
Fellow of the Royal Photographic Society

Preface

I was born on Amami Island and lived there for the first ten years of my life. Although it has been more than fifty years since I left this island, the passing years bring back vivid memories of my early days there; more than anything else about it, I remember the sight of pure white egrets dancing in the deep green, ever-moist rice paddies.

Ever since learning to use a camera, I have observed and studied these birds. On my first visit to an egret colony, I was overwhelmed by the magnificent spectacle before me. A vast number of birds ruffled and spread their lacelike, brilliant white feathers. Chicks cried out and huddled together in nests, or fought fiercely for control of a mother egret's food-filled beak. For some time, I stood rooted to the ground, watching with amazement.

Since that first view of an egret colony, I have harbored an impatient longing for spring, rushing to egret colonies for that first stunning sight of the birds at daybreak. The birds have come to seem human to me at times, such as when I witnessed a parent bird patiently protecting a chick from the incessant summer rain. I have spent long, lonely nights in a foul-smelling, mosquito-infested forest just for a glimpse of a colony of egrets, and have shouldered more than forty pounds of photo equipment up dark, steep hills, awaiting sunrise under a shower of bird droppings. I pursued the white egret all over Japan, taking photographs in a soaking summer rain or in a typhoon, or spending a day in a tree in the scorching sun without a water bottle, after which I lost my voice due to dehydration, or even in a snowstorm during which I photographed with numb fingers.

In Japan, the white egret is a popular motif in painting and literature, in haiku and song, as well as an object of worship. Many place names are associated with the egret: Shirasagi (White Egret), Sagisu (Egret Sand Bar), Sagikke (Egret Pond), and Sagijima (Egret Island). The Japanese word for egret, *sagi*, is believed to be related to a word that means "uproar," no doubt a reference to the egret's raucous calls.

Although the Japanese people hold the egret in great affection, the egret's sphere of activity increasingly overlaps that of man. The diminished populations of the birds—because of environmental changes due to land development and deaths caused by fertilizer-contaminated food—have been making a comeback. Some foraging grounds have been restored, and fertilizer regulations have been tightened. Even so, egrets continue to be killed or driven away by neighboring humans, who complain about the raucous noise of the flocks, the damage done by the birds to young rice plants, the foul odor of the droppings, and the birds' hunting of fish in carefully stocked fish preserves.

Of the estimated nine thousand species of birds in the world, sixty-two belong to the egret family. Eighteen species of egret have been sighted in Japan, the majority of them migrating there during the spring; thirteen species of egret breed in Japan.

Known for their long bills and necks, white bodies, and slender legs, the graceful forms of these birds can be seen at water's edge in large flocks. Although some colonies may consist of a single species, in the majority of colonies a variety of species can be found. In these mixed nesting colonies, there might be great egrets, intermediate egrets, little egrets, cattle egrets, along with black-crowned night herons and perhaps gray herons and great cormorants, all nesting together. Found from Hokkaido to Kyusu, the numerous egret colonies consist predominately, however, of little egrets and black-crowned night herons. Great and intermediate egrets only compose about 1.3 percent of any given colony.

The distinguishing features of the great, intermediate, and little egret are body size, bill shape and color, lore (the area between the eye and the bill), and breeding plumage. Standing about ninety centimeters tall, the great egret is the largest of the three species. The little egret is just sixty centimeters tall, while the intermediate egret stands in between at about seventy centimeters. The lores of the great egret are yellowish green and its bill yellow; in breeding season, the lores turn bluish green and the bill becomes black. The lores of the intermediate egret remain yellow throughout the year, though the normally yellow bill turns black for mating season. The lores of the little egret turn from yellow to crimson during mating season; its bill remains black all year long. The little egret is the most easily identifiable of the three species. During mating season its distinctive yellow feet become tinged with red, and two long feathers grow down the back of the bird's head. Also unique to the little egret is the curl at the ends of its breeding plumage.

Eye color for all three species is grayish yellow; during the mating season, the irises of the great and intermediate egret turn bright red for a short period of time. The spring color changes of bill, lore, feet, and eye color are particularly brilliant when the birds choose mates.

All three species produce special strawlike feathers that decorate their backs during breeding season. The splendor of this display is said to be the white egret's greatest beauty. These feathers were once so highly prized by Western women as hat ornaments that the white egret came dangerously close to extinction.

With the arrival of spring and the mating season, migratory and nonmigratory birds begin gathering at nesting colonies. After choosing mates and building nests in treetops, the birds lay their eggs and begin the laborious task of raising their young. At the end of summer, when the chicks have matured, the birds migrate to a warmer place for the winter months.

I have taken more than one hundred thousand photographs of egrets and felt deeply the frustration of being an amateur photographer. The task of capturing the true beauty of the lustrous, snow-white egret on film has been completely beyond my capabilities, although I have continued to take pictures of them. As difficult as this task might be, the sight of a mother protecting her chick or the drama of a chick first leaving the nest continues to touch me. I have felt a need to understand the egret's movements and behavior, their enduring existence, and to share what I have learned about them with others.

Although it is next to impossible to chronicle in their entirety the lifestyles of the great, intermediate, and little egret, I have attempted to be as accurate as possible. My observations serve as only one dimension, while the records of my predecessors serve as another. Nothing would please me more than if this book were to serve as an introduction to not only the white egret but to birds in general.

Acknowledgments

I would like to express my thanks to the following people: Doctor Yamagishi Tetsu, assistant professor of biology, Osaka Municipal University, for revision assistance; Mr. Fujioka Masashi, graduate student at Dodaigaku University, for his invaluable assistance; Ms. Abe Masatsune, chief editor of publishing at Yamato Keikoku Company, for publishing services; and Mr. Kumagaya for design.

Lastly, I would like to thank the many people whom I have not named for their gracious assistance with document acquisition and photography. I would like to express my deepest gratitude to all of them.

9 *A circling great egret begins its descent into the woods.*

10   *Little egrets in spring.*

11 *Morning flight of the great egret.*

12 *Intermediate egret (summer).*

13 *Still wet from the previous night's rain a great egret displays its breeding plumage.*

▶14 *Breeding plumage of the intermediate egret.*

15 *The great egret displays breeding plumage not only for courtship purposes but as a ritual greeting to its mate upon return to the nest.*

16 *Courting behavior of great egrets.*

17   *Breeding plumage display of the great egret (right) and little egret (left).*

18 *Lakeshore sunrise (great egret).*

19   *Display of the intermediate egret.*

20 *The intermediate egret with brown-tinged feathers. Because the breeding plumage is longer than the regular plumage it is often dirtied by muddy water.*

21 *Intermediate egret.*

22 *Intermediate egret.*

23   *Intermediate egret stretching its wings.*

24 *Preening intermediate egret.*

25 *Preening intermediate egret.*

26 *Preening little egret.*

27 *Preening little egret.*

28 *A great egret fledgling sheltered by its parent. By this time the breeding plumage is beginning to molt.*

29 *Great egret couple.*

30 *Little egret.*

31 *Little egret.*

33 *Great egret.*

34 *A flock of great egrets takes flight in autumn.*

35 *Preroosting assembly of great, intermediate, and little egrets.*

36 *Due to meager food supplies, little egrets quarrel ceaselessly over artificially stocked fish.*

▶ 37 *Preroosting assembly of little egrets.*

38 *Great egret preening in the early morning.*

Daily Life

The annual cycle of the egret's life consists of migration to the breeding site, mating, brooding, and, once the chicks mature, migration to a winter retreat. But it is their daily habits — preening, vocalization, foraging, moving about, fighting, and flocking — that reveal the most about the egret. I have watched them, fascinated, for hundreds of hours.

Preening

The egret's preening behaviors — head scratching, preening, and bathing — all keep feathers clean and neatly arranged and distribute protective oils. Patches of powdery down under the egret's breast and flank feathers reduce to a fine dust that when spread on the plumage by the bird's head and bill during preening protects the feathers from the slime of fish and other prey. The dust soaks up the slime, which is then removed when the feathers are combed with the pectinated comblike inside of the egret's middle claw.

In preening, the bird rearranges each feather by lightly biting it and pulling along its length with a combing motion. The bird moves from feather to feather removing dirt and parasites; it also shakes its body and beats its wings to fluff flattened feathers or to speed drying after bathing.

Vocalization

The most distinctive feature of the egret's voice is its harsh, unpleasant sound. The saying "Nature gives but one gift" certainly applies to the white egret, whose unexpectedly terrible voice contrasts sharply with its beautiful appearence. Although slight differences can be discerned, the great, intermediate, and little egret all share the same low, nasal hoarseness. During the mating season, vocalization becomes louder and more highly pitched. The birds have different cries for calls, warnings, threats, cries of fright, fighting, mating, awakening, and entering the roost. Both the male and female white egret vocalize. And, of course, the vocalization of adult birds differs from that of the chicks.

The noise in the colonies continues day and night. The egret's contagious *goah, goah*
is a constant communication between roost members. When an intruder enters the nesting colony, the surprised birds cry *goah, goah* and take to the air in fright. Among egret flocks this type of panic occurs frequently.

During the incubation period the roost is strikingly quieter, although a threatening *guoo* can be heard whenever a member of the flock approaches the wrong nest. Approximately one day before hatching, a weak *pi, pi* can be heard coming from inside the egg. Several days after the chicks hatch, the *chit, chit* quickly strengthens to louder, more vehement cries of *gya, gya, gero, gero*. Sibling chicks quarreling and begging for food forget about chirping after feeding, and grow quiet.

Away from the roost and while in midflight egrets rarely vocalize. One day when I was in the field I heard a low, threatening *guoo* nearby. Turning to look, I saw a little egret take flight to challenge a bird some yards ahead. While continuing its threatening cries, the little egret flew over my head in pursuit of its opponent. On another occasion, while observing a flock of little egrets foraging in a fish pond, I heard the warning cries of a bird in their midst and watched as they tensed in preparation for flight.

Foraging

Throughout the year the principal ingredients of the white egrets' diet are small fish, American crayfish, insects, spiders, and other small creatures. Most prey is swallowed whole if it is small enough. Mixed in with the white droppings covering the ground beneath the roost are pieces of regurgitated food dropped by fighting and jostling chicks or vomited up by frightened chicks, and disgorged indigestible material. By examining this matter it is possible to get some idea of the egret's diet, although the contents of the egret's stomach must be examined for a detailed understanding of the bird's diet. One report compiled after such an examination revealed sixty-seven loaches, frogs, tadpoles, dragonflies, and water beetle larva in the stomach of a little egret. Depending on the region in which it lives, the same egret species may have strikingly different diets.

Although white egrets primarily feed on freshwater animals, they occasionally are seen foraging along coastal waters during low tide. The development of salt processing glands seems to be stimulated by the consumption of sea life; in this way, egrets adapt to the excess consumption of salt. They rarely drink water, for the surface moisture and body fluids of prey provide the birds with much of the water they need.

The egret's long neck structure, which allows it to thrust its head in vertical movements, and the sharply pointed bill, perfectly suited for catching small prey, make the egret a skillful hunter. The unobstructed view of the tip of its bill enables the egret to aim its thrusts with amazing accuracy. Further enhancing the egret's hunting skills are its small head, wide-set eyes, and long bill.

Foraging techniques differ somewhat depending on the species. In general, egrets forage in shallows and around the water's edge. Standing immobile with its neck tucked in, an egret will stare fixedly at the water's surface and wait for prey to swim by. Or, stepping slowly and cautiously in the shallows, the egret will quickly seize any moving prey with a swift forward thrust and quickly swallow it whole. The first time I witnessed an egret swallowing its prey I was astounded. After catching a large fish, the bird slowly inched the struggling prey down its throat. The fish was so large that I could see the bird's throat thicken as it went down.

Egrets occasionally forage alone but more commonly forage in flocks. In winter, when the food supply is meager, members of the flock jealously watch one another in anticipation of stealing captured prey. Such scenes can be especially humorous when a bird unexpectedly comes upon a large prey. As the other birds flock greedily, the lucky captor scrambles to escape with its catch. Foraging in flocks appears to have advantages over foraging alone. For example, when a flock of cattle egrets forages in a grassy field, one bird will lead the rest of the flock. As the lead egret chases after insects, it startles and dislodges other prey that birds following behind may easily consume. This instinctive cooperation among cattle egrets enables each member of the flock to hunt more efficiently. Furthermore, the flock spends less time on the lookout for predators than a bird hunting alone and, thus, can spend more time foraging. On the other hand, birds foraging in flocks have a greater tendency to quarrel; if one member approaches another too closely a skirmish will erupt. This is especially true if a member of the flock moves away to forage alone. Any other birds that approach are quickly driven away.

Moving its legs deliberately and rhythmically, the little egret will stir up the water's bottom in order to dislodge prey. This instinctive leg movement appears to develop at an early age; I have even seen little egret hatchlings moving in this way while pecking at regurgitated prey in the nest. Sighting prey while in midflight, the little egret will make a sudden landing and run swiftly after the animal. Similarly, the egret will swoop low and skim the surface of a lake, seizing any prey that it comes upon. During particularly harsh winters when food supplies are scarce, little egrets are often caught stealing dead fish from fishing boats, and all three species have been seen stealing frozen sardines left by game officials for migrating cranes.

Feeding on insects and aquatic life, the intermediate egret forages both at the water's edge and in dry grassy fields. From a dietary point of view, therefore, the intermediate egret must compete with both little and cattle egrets for foraging territory. This competition could be one explanation for the decreasing intermediate egret population and the greater abundance of little and cattle egrets.

The great egret prefers to forage alone in large bodies of water that have relatively unobstructed aerial views. Flying low over the water's surface, the bird will make spectacular dives for prey. One study reported that the great egret is able to associate bread crumbs floating on the water's surface with prey. Thus, birds seeing such crumbs will investigate for feeding fish.

Feeding primarily on the insects and spiders found in grassy fields and paddies, the cattle egret differs from the other white egret species. Because large animals such as cattle, horses, sheep, rhinoceros, and elephants attract many insects, the birds are often seen nearby and, thus, have been named "cattle egrets." Cattle egrets also commonly feed on the parasites that infest these animals. The animals in turn benefit from this mutually advantageous relationship as the birds not only rid them of parasites, but alert them to approaching danger as well.

During the incubation and brooding period, parent birds must stay at the nest as well as gather food for both themselves and their hatchlings. Driven day after day by the need for food, parent birds exhaust their physical strength. It is believed that the high death rate of great and intermediate egrets following the autumn migration is due, in part, to the extreme physical demands of providing for offspring. During the incubation period and the early stage just after hatching, parents alternately engage in foraging. When chicks are approximately two weeks old and have acquired a thicker plumage, parents no longer need to keep the nest warm, and both can gather prey to feed their increasingly voracious chicks.

At dusk, just as white egrets return to the roost, black-crowned night herons head out in twos and threes to the foraging grounds. As herons commute to and from the foraging site, the evening sky resounds with the birds' peculiar *quock*. At dawn the herons return to the roost. Deciding to spend the night sheltered under some trees in which a heron flock had built its nests, I pitched my tent and settled down for the night. Although the ceaseless chirping of the chicks made it difficult to fall asleep, I was just drifting off when parent birds suddenly began returning to the roost with food for their young. The demanding cries of the hungry chicks along with the constant patter of bird droppings hitting my tent kept me awake throughout the night.

Although the black-crowned night heron is nocturnal, it occasionally forages during the day. During the mating season, much of its courtship activity occurs while the sun is up. The majority of the time, however, the black-crowned night heron feeds at night. Because egrets and herons hunt at the same foraging sites, the day and night alternation between the two groups not only enables the birds to make efficient use of the feeding grounds but avoids territory disputes as well. In this way, nature takes care that its resources are not wasted.

Moving About

Although white egrets rest, mate, and roost in treetops, they spend a great deal of time on the ground. The birds primarily move about by flying. All egrets, however, have the ability to walk, run, and even swim.

The snowy white wingspan of the white egret is especially beautiful. Unlike smaller birds, white egrets are hampered by the great length and width of their wings and cannot fly great distances, take off quickly, or make sharp spins and turns. Like almost all birds, however, white egrets are able to soar and glide. In order to swoop or make a dive, the egret beats its wings in quick succession, checks its speed, and then tucks its wings tightly and aims downward. The breathtaking splendor of the bird's tailspin as it wheels and dives is reminiscent of a difficult gymnastics maneuver.

Although egrets often glide to conserve energy, they normally fly in a straight line with slow, rhythmic wing beats. Flocking egrets fly in tight formation; during flight— the average speed is about forty kilometers per hour—the neck is tucked back and the head is drawn between the shoulders. When issuing a warning in midflight, the egret stretches its neck straight out and assumes the appearance of a crane. To maintain balance, the egret untucks its neck when taking off and landing.

When traveling by foot, the egret alternately lifts each leg in a slow, deliberate fashion, gripping the ground with spread claws as it moves forward. When fleeing, chasing prey, or attacking a rival, the egret often runs along the ground with small swift steps.

Frequently the egret rests standing on one foot with its body positioned slightly forward. When summer heat becomes unbearable, the exhausted little egret will sprawl out on a tree branch or crouch on the ground. Some sit for long hours in water trying to stay cool.

Fighting

Much of a bird's life is spent fighting to maintain mating, nesting, foraging, and other territories. Although flocking white egrets appear to quarrel ceaselessly, the fighting is rarely very fierce. Glaring at its opponent, an angry egret will assume a threatening posture by opening its bill slightly and bristling its plumage. Most of the fights that become physically violent develop over territorial rights to foraging grounds. Some quarreling birds settle their arguments with a compromise; more commonly, however, one bird will quickly concede victory to its opponent, thus avoiding injury and exhaustion. Occasionally two stubborn birds will remain enemies for their entire lives.

Individual roosting territories in the colony are extremely small and closely spaced, causing frequent quarrels to erupt. If the egret feels that its perch is threatened it will persistently warn others away by crying out *gyak* in a sharp voice. In the open field, egrets do not quarrel to the extent they do in the roost. The first stage of a fight between two little egrets begins with threatening cries of *goah, goah* as the rivals stretch their necks and point their bills skyward. While continuing to emit a hoarse *goah*, the birds will try to intimidate one another with threatening postures. The fighting may also continue in the air, although the grappling rivals soon fall back to the ground. On one occasion I observed the winner climb onto its opponent's back to signal victory.

It is not unusual to see sibling chicks fighting among themselves. Once, I heard the demanding screeches of a hungry chick come to a halt as it unexpectedly fell into a nest directly below its own, where it was quickly and furiously attacked by the chicks of the nest. I have also seen a cattle egret chick kill its own sibling. Although I have never observed interspecies fighting between great and little egrets, I have seen young black-crowned night herons steal chicks from the unguarded nest of a great egret.

Flocking

White egrets flock all year round. Even after the mating season, they continue to roost and forage together in large groups. Migration also occurs in flocks. It was once believed that the flock was led by an appointed leader. Simultaneous take-offs, preroosting assemblies, roosting, and other such flocking habits were thought to be controlled by a lead bird. The perfectly coordinated movement of the flock seemed to support this theory. Now, however, it is believed that each member is so closely attuned to the movement of the other members that, with each bird anticipating the other's movement, the flock moves in a smoothly coordinated wave.

When they return to the roost after a day's foraging, egrets gather in preroosting assemblies before entering the roost. It is believed that the colony acts as an information center or news exchange on the condition and locations of foraging sites. For example, birds that have had little luck foraging the previous day are often seen the following morning leaving with birds that have been successful. This theory, however, has yet to be fully examined.

Although flocking habits provide protection and assist foraging, communal living has drawbacks, one of which is that the conspicuously large size of the egret colony attracts intruders, leaving the birds constantly fearful and tense. I have witnessed a frightened flock helplessly protesting as raiding kites snatched up egret chicks. The flock, however, reduces the risk of predators by choosing sites that offer the greatest protection. By building their nests in thick forests or bamboo groves, the birds are less visible and less accessible.

Plumage color may be important to the survival of a species. If it is, how does their white plumage affect the existence of the white egret? The sharp-sighted egret may use the pure whiteness of the plumage to identify other flock members. They probably also distinguish enemies by their lack of whiteness. One wonders though, how the egret distinguishes beween friendly and potentially dangerous situations. I have seen cattle and little egrets unhesitatingly forage around a farm tractor in operation, but take flight when they spot a distant cameraman. What is the motivation behind such behavior, I wonder?

39 *Leaving the roost before sunrise, the hunt for food begins.*

40 *Little egret at the end of the rainy season. Although the birds are disliked for trampling rice seedlings, they are tolerated because they feed upon American crayfish, a pest that threatens rice crops.*

▶ 41 *Foraging little egret.*

42~44 *This foraging bird positions struggling prey so it can be swallowed whole.*

43

44

45 *The rhythmic exaggerated steps of the little egret stir up the water's bottom to dislodge prey. In one month, both the head feathers and the breeding plumage have begun to develop in preparation for the mating season.*

46 *Foraging great egrets look on enviously as one bird successfully catches a large fish.*

47 *Poised near a lotus field, with the passing of the mating season, this great egret's breeding plumage has molted and its bill is once again yellow.*

▶48 *A great egret flying low over the river's surface makes a spectacular dive for a large fish. The great egret displays a greater tendency to hunt alone.*

49 *Little egrets feeding in a river.*

50 *A great egret circles over partially submerged coral formations washed in by the tide at Amami Island.*

51 *Two great egrets forage in the sea. Although white egrets normally prefer to forage in fresh water, the birds are able easily to adjust to the increase of salt in their diet. With the approach of the mating season one bird's bill has turned completely black, while the other's remains unchanged.*

52 *Although the black-crowned night heron is primarily nocturnal, it is often seen foraging for food during the daylight hours.*

53 *Cattle egrets commonly feed on parasites that infest large animals. The birds are frequently sighted in close proximity to such animals as cattle, horses, sheep, rhinoceros, and elephants. (The animals also benefit from this relationship because the birds rid them of parasites and alert them to approaching danger.)*
The cattle egret on the left still displays some breeding plumage.

54 *A flock of cattle egrets forage in a rice paddy. Indigenous to the African and Asian continents, cattle egrets crossed the Atlantic Ocean at the turn of the century and spread across the American continent.*

55 *Feeding primarily on insects that live in the rice paddy, the cattle egret occasionally eats other aquatic creatures.*

57 *Preening intermediate egret.*

56 *A little egret engaged in one of a variety of preening postures.*

58 *The yellow bill and thinning breeding feathers of this preening intermediate egret indicate the end of summer.*

62 *Preening intermediate egret.*

63 *A great egret bathes in a lotus paddy.*

Great egrets dispute territorial rights to a feeding ground.

65

66

68

73

71~76 Little egrets fighting in open
ground begin by stretching their
necks, pointing their bills skyward, and emitting harsh croaks.
In an effort to intimidate its opponent each bird holds its own in the
scuffle. Normally however, the
fighting seldom persists for long, as
one bird will soon retreat.

75

76

77

78

77~78 *The close spacing of individual nesting areas in the colonies provides the egrets with ample opportunity to argue. The sharp, persistent screeches of quarreling birds never seems to cease.*

79 *In this rare fight between two little egrets, the winner climbs upon its opponent's back to signal victory. Confrontations occasionally escalate to pecking and shoving matches.*

80

80~81 *Little egrets commonly flock together when foraging for food.*

Spring

Spring, the most colorful time of year, is when white egrets arrive at the nesting colonies and begin preparation for mating, the activity most crucial to the continued existence of the species. The springtime growth of breeding plumage enhances the white egret's beauty.

Arrival

The arrival time of white egrets differs from species to species, region to region, and year to year, but in general the birds have arrived at the nesting colonies by the end of March. The great egret usually arrives first, followed by the black-crowned night heron. Close behind come the little and intermediate egret. Finally, one month after the arrival of the great egret, the cattle egret reaches the colony, signalling the end of spring migration.

Recently, the average size of a colony has decreased. The majority of egret colonies have 500 birds or less and it is extremely rare to find a colony that exceeds 2,000 members. The winter roosts of nonmigratory birds rarely have more than 500 members. The more than two-hundred-year-old egret colony in Noda, once a national monument populated by tens of thousands of egrets, was closed in 1971 as a result of a population drop. This has been interpreted as a silent warning—a pollution indicator—that the environment these wild birds depend on is drastically deteriorating.

Courtship

The first few days after arrival are spent at the foraging sites. Soon after, however, feeding is limited to the afternoon hours and the nesting colonies come alive with courtship activity.

Great, intermediate, and little egrets differ very little in courting and mating behavior. Because there are no visible differences between the male and female of the same species, it is believed that egrets distinguish gender by posture and behavior. For human observers, the only way to ascertain the sex of an egret is by watching the act of copulation or waiting to see which bird lays the eggs. The male great egret, however, appears to be slightly larger than the female.

The greatest beauty of the white egret is the splendor of the lacy breeding plumage ruffled up in a dazzling courtship display. The strawlike feathers that grow on the backs of the great, the intermediate, and the little egret are particularly beautiful. Although both male and female egrets grow special breeding plumage on their backs, only the male bird creates a variety of displays accompanied by a loud clamor during the courtship period. The display is not limited to impressing a potential mate during mating, however, but also functions as a form of greeting when a bird returns to the nest after foraging, relieves its partner of nesting duties, or delivers nesting materials. Both male and female egrets perform this greeting ritual display.

As with most migratory birds, the male white egret arrives at the mating colony before the females in order to establish courtship territory. When the females arrive, the birds begin the process of selecting mates.

A courting couple will often gently bite each other's heads, touch and intertwine bills, and preen each other as a way to maintain the bond between them. Soon after selecting a mate, egrets begin to build their nests. (The touching of bills probably developed from nest building behavior—passing nesting materials from bill to bill—rather than from courtship or foraging behaviors.) Because egrets are extremely timid during this time, and take to the air whenever an intruder approaches, colonies should be left alone until mating is over.

Taking only twenty seconds, copulation is extremely brief. The female crouches forward resting her breast on a branch or the nest to maintain her balance while the male perches precariously on her back. During copulation both birds emit a hoarse froglike croak. For the most part, egrets are monogamous and stay with one mate throughout the spring and summer. However, copulation frequently occurs outside the mated pair. I have seen, for example, a male little egret leave its eggs unattended for a brief minute while he flew to a nearby nest to copulate with a neighbor. Despite "extramarital" activities, the bond between mated couples remains strong.

Because "extramarital" copulation is not uncommon, it is impossible to determine the male parentage of the chicks. The possibility exists, therefore, that the male egret provides for chicks that are not his own. At the same time, his own offspring may be raised by another couple. The ability of stronger males to copulate with females other than their chosen mate appears to have the salutary effect of maintaining a strong gene pool, contributing to the continued survival of the species. At this point, however, knowledge and understanding concerning the "extramarital" copulation of monogamous birds is still very limited. Further research is required in this relatively new field of study.

Although I have not observed cross-mating of egret species in the wild, I have seen the mixed-breed chick of a cattle and little egret in captivity.

It is believed that juvenile birds begin mating the year following their birth. Even when mating activity reaches its peak in the colonies, there are birds that remain in trees normally used for the winter roost. These birds are most likely slow to develop sexually or are for some reason unable to mate.

Nest Building

Made of twigs, the crudely constructed egret nest is shaped like a large, shallow bowl. Going from branch to branch with her mate, looking for a suitable location to build, the female makes the final selection by grasping the branch where she wants to build. Often, this site is at a fork in a branch. At best, the nesting territory is out of the range of other pecking birds, but is typically much smaller than each bird's individual territory prior to mating.

Once a site has been selected, the male immediately begins to collect building materials while the female remains behind to guard their territory. Collecting twigs from the ground and breaking green twigs off nearby trees, the male delivers them to the waiting female, who skillfully constructs the nest. The male usually stays within a five-hundred-meter radius when gathering nesting materials. When the opportunity arises, foraging males will steal materials from nearby nests or even make off with the entire structure. Many egret couples prefer to repair old nests left from the previous year rather than build their own. The collection of nesting materials continues even after the chicks are hatched. Because the nest is not in need of repair, this behavior appears to be performed primarily out of habit.

Once the most desirable nesting locations in the treetops are selected, the lower nesting sites are then chosen. Thus, due to their early arrival, great egrets and black-crowned night herons typically occupy the tops of trees. Slower to arrive, intermediate and cattle egrets are often seen wedging their nests in the few remaining open sites on lower branches.

Nesting

Approximately one week after the couple begins to build their nest, the female lays her first egg. Although the nest is not yet completed, enough construction has been done for egg-laying to begin. Even after the start of the incubation period, the couple continues to lay eggs while completing construction of the nest. The egret's eggs are shaped much like those of a chicken and are an unblemished beautiful bluish green color. As the days pass, however, the color begins to fade and toward the end of the incubation period the eggs are discolored and dirty.

During incubation, the parent bird straddles the eggs and gently covers them. Occasionally standing to rotate the eggs, the parent will thrust its bill between the eggs to make sure they do not rub against one another. This behavior ensures that each egg is evenly warmed and that the embryo does not stick to the shell.

Parents alternate incubation duties so that one parent can feed while the other keeps the nest warm, although the female parent spends a greater amount of time sitting on the nest. When the foraging parent returns to the nest, its mate quietly rises and moves away. During this exchange of duties, the couple performs the greeting ritual display and, occasionally, they copulate.

During the incubation period, egrets are extremely nervous and hot-tempered, and the bird becomes stern and menacing as it guards its territory. If another bird happens to trespass, the parent bristles its feathers and issues a domineering *guoo* at the transgressing bird. At the slightest hint of danger, the parent stretches its neck out, although it rarely flees. Although the parent bird may leave the nest upon seeing a human, it does not fly far. While keeping a close eye on the intruder, the parent soon returns to the nest and continues warming the eggs.

82 *After selecting mates, the irises of the intermediate egrets begin to return to their normal color.*

83 *Spring wading. The color changes of this great egret are at their peak.*

85 *A foraging little egret escapes to the treetops when a man approaches.*

◄84 *Five great egrets and one little egret (left). All but one great egret have turned color for the mating season.*

86 *Little egret.*

87   *A great egret stands in a lotus field.*

88 *The first days after the spring arrival are spent at the foraging sites. Soon, however, foraging is limited to the afternoons, and the roost comes alive with courting activity.*

89 *Display of the great egret.*

90 *Mated little egrets select a site for nest building.*

91 *Mated intermediate egrets.*

92

93

92~96 *Typical mating behavior. Copulation frequently occurs outside of the mated pair.*

94

95
96

78—79

97   *Intermediate egrets copulating.*

98 *The female little egret rests on the nest or a tree branch while the male balances precariously on her back. Copulation takes approximately twenty seconds. Although this couple has had several eggs the nest is still unfinished. When the incubation period begins, the nest will be completed.*

99   *Intermediate egret returns to the roost with nesting material.*

100   *An intermediate egret breaks branches for its nest. After choosing a nesting location,*
      the male leaves to gather materials while the female guards their new territory.

101   *Great egret steals from a neighbor.*

▶102   *Out of habit, the birds continue to*
       gather nesting materials even after
       the new chicks have hatched.

103 *A great egret holds nesting material.*

104 *The female constructs the nest out of the branches gathered by the male.*

105 *Black-crowned night heron passes a branch to his mate.*

106~109 *Intermediate egret couples display reassurance and affection by gently biting, touching bills, and preening each other.*

106

107

▶110~111 *The elegant form of the egret becomes stern and menacing as it watchfully guards its territory while incubating its eggs.*

112 *The parent bird keeping the nest warm occasionally stands to change the position of the eggs and make sure that they are not rubbing against each other.*

113 *A bird relieves its mate from incubating duties. The couple continues to copulate even after several eggs have been laid.*

Summer

During the summer months egret chicks hatch, develop, and eventually become independent. For the first months of summer, the colonies are full of life as hungry chicks cry for food and young birds chase after their parents. Soon, however, the fledglings reach maturity and the colonies gradually grow quieter.

Hatching

The chicks hatch within three to four weeks of being laid. Receiving no help from the parent bird, the chick pecks at the brittle egg shell until it is free. Born with a wet covering of down feathers, the hatchling is unable to lift its head or stand up and lies exhausted on its stomach with its eyes closed. After about thirty hours, the thin down dries and the now fluffy hatchling begins to look like a bird. Because the eggs are not all laid at the same time, they hatch one after another and the colony gradually becomes animated with the cries of the new chicks.

Once a chick has hatched the parent bird removes the broken eggshell from the nest and disposes of it.

Brooding

Egret chicks are unable to leave the nest and are dependent on their parents for warmth and food. From the beginning, both parents perform brooding duties, crouching over the newly hatched chicks with both wings extended, so that the chicks can nestle between the parent's legs and under its breast. This posture protects the chicks from pouring rain and harsh sunlight.

After about ten days, the chicks produce a thicker covering of white feathers and their legs and bill grow thicker and longer. By this time they can recognize danger. Upon seeing a human form, for example, chicks will crouch down and sneak to the far side of the nest in an attempt to hide. After two weeks, both parents stay away from the nest for longer periods, though even three-week-old chicks will be sheltered by a parent during a heavy rain.

Gathering and storing prey in its craw from early morning on, the parent bird returns to the roost to feed its offspring. Before entering the nest, the parent threads its way among nests close to its own and surveys the roost as though checking to make sure all is well. Only after this ritual will the parent return to the nest to feed its chicks.

Newly hatched chicks lay close to regurgitated prey so that they may peck at it during waking hours. Unlike many birds that supply water to their offspring via plumage moistened at a water hole, the egret does not provide water for its chicks, perhaps because the water content of regurgitated prey is sufficient. From nine to eleven days after hatching the chicks are fed orally. Initially the chicks quietly wait to receive food from their parent's mouth, but as they grow they become increasingly vocal in their demands for food. As soon as the parent bird approaches the nest, the impatient chicks stretch their necks and hungrily open their bills. Crying *gyak, gyak, gero, gero,* eager chicks throng about the parent the instant it enters the nest, seizing its bill violently and often unbalancing the parent. The parent is unable to lift its head until feeding is over. Once the frenzied feeding ends, both parent and chicks rest quietly for a short period.

When it becomes time for chicks to leave the nest, the parent changes the feeding pattern to entice chicks out of the nest. Placing some food in the nest, the parent then moves away, luring the hungry chicks out of the nest. Following the parent, the hungry chicks thus increase their radius of movement. After a few days, the parent bird positions itself on a branch nearby the nest and waits for the hungry chicks to approach. When one chick leaps to the parent, it receives a morsel of food. Soon after, the rest of the chicks follow hesitantly. Once they have learned to maneuver through the tree, walking and leaping from branch to branch, the chicks no longer wait in the nest to be fed. They strengthen their bills biting and pecking at branches while they wait for their parents to return with prey.

The daily life of a young egret is rarely tranquil. Chicks have been known to tumble from the nest, perhaps in the commotion caused by a human or a dog invading the roost. Sometimes, a heavy rain will dampen a young bird's wings, causing it to slip off a branch because of their unaccustomed weight. I have seen eggs and chicks knocked from a nest by the sudden gust caused by the parent bird taking flight. Chicks that fall from the nest wander beneath the roost until they die; they cannot return to the nest on their own, nor can the parent bird save them once they have fallen. Chicks also die of exposure when parent birds are away from the nest for long periods of time. Egrets learn to fear kites and crows early, as both species steal egret chicks from the nest.

However, most chicks' deaths are caused by food deficiency. When food is scarce, only the chicks that hatch first survive; those that hatch later die within the first few days. However, different hatching times prevent an entire generation of chicks from being destroyed by food scarcity. Nevertheless, survival in the wild is extremely precarious, with fewer than 20 percent of chicks reaching maturity.

Development

Three weeks after hatching the chicks have grown considerably. The chick's body and legs develop more quickly than its wings and plumage. Once they can walk, chicks excrete their droppings over the edge of the nest. Before that, they excrete in the nest; because the nest is loosely woven together the fluid matter leaks out and the nest stays fairly clean. The young egret's wings are still weak and they practice flapping their wings vigorously in the nest and while walking and jumping from branch to branch. Soon, the nests will have served their purpose and will be discarded. Before long, the young birds are able to step off a branch and, with furious flapping, keep themselves aloft.

Thirty-five to forty days after hatching, the chicks make their first successful flight. The young birds no longer wait on branches for returning parents, but fly out to meet the parent as soon as it approaches the roost. Although the young birds are physically mature and can be mistaken for adults, they still depend on their parents for food. Parents gradually distance themselves from their chicks and try to avoid the now-competing young birds as they beg for food. From the end of June to the beginning of July, the colonies are at their busiest, with the young birds chasing after their elusive parents and demanding to be fed. Gradually, delighting in their ability to fly, they increase their flying distance and in doing so they soon gain the ability to reach the foraging site. At last, fifty to sixty days after hatching, the young bird is fully independent and accompanies the adult flock to far-away feeding grounds. Soon the bond between the parents and their offspring fades, but in the gregarious egret colony it seems unlikely that the parents completely forget their offspring. Once a young bird assumes its own roosting perch, it does not look to other birds for food or assistance nor do parent birds continue providing for their offspring.

By mid-July both young and adult birds leave the roost early in the morning to hunt for prey. Only sleeping black-crowned night herons and a few lonely underdeveloped chicks occupy the roost during the afternoon hours. At dusk, the egrets return and the whole area resounds with loud calls and the noisy flapping of wings.

114 *Parent great egret with its fledgling.*

115 *After three to four weeks, the chicks break out of the eggs. Born with a downy covering, the chicks lie exhausted in the nest. After approximately thirty hours the down dries and the chick begins to look like a bird (little egret).*

116 *This newly hatched little egret chick naps next to prey regurgitated by the parent bird. Surprisingly few chicks starve to death after the first week.*

117 *The incubation period begins when the first and second eggs are laid. After the first chick hatches it takes from one to six days for the rest of the chicks to hatch.*

118 *As the parent bird approaches the nest, these little egret chicks stretch out their necks in anticipation and clamor to be fed. The little egret produces from four to seven eggs, one every day and a half.*

119 *After nine to eleven days the hatchlings are fed orally.*

121 *Parent bird seems to be sighing with relief after a violent feeding.*

120 *The parent bird's bill is seized violently by hungry chicks that refuse to let go until the feeding is over.*

122 *Display upon returning to the nest. The greeting ritual display and the courtship display serve entirely different functions.*

123 *Relief from brooding duties.*

124 *Parent birds and chicks crowd the nests. Once the most desirable nesting sites in the treetops are selected, the lower, less desirable sites are chosen.*

125 *Little egrets fish in a marsh.*

126 *A little egret parent stoically warms the nest during a summer downpour. Sitting in a crouching position the bird holds its wings away from its body, and space is made for the chicks underneath the breast and between the legs.*

127 *An intermediate egret returns to the nest after foraging. The damage to the molting breeding plumage is clearly visible.*

▶128 *Intermediate egret fledglings.*

129 *Although night has fallen, these egrets continue to forage.*

130 *Great egret parent and chick.*

131 *The day arrives when the chick leaves the nest. In order to entice the chick out of the nest,*
the parent bird changes the feeding patterns. First placing only a little food in the nest, the
parent bird then moves away and the chick follows. In this way, the chick increases its
radius of movement.

132 *Little egret fledglings venture away from the nest. Climbing up the dead tree was no problem, but getting down is another matter.*

133 *Marshland; the egret's bill serves a wide variety of functions, for everything from fighting to foraging.*

134 *Approaching maturity, these little egret fledglings jump from branch to branch in youthful frolic.*

135 *Losing a quarrel, this chick falls from the nest. The parent bird is unable to save the chick, nor can the chick return to the nest on its own. It will wander about under the trees until finally it dies.*

136 *Little egret fledgling. The legs develop more quickly than the wings, and the plumage is slowest to grow.*

137 *Thirty-five to forty days after hatching, the great egret fledgling makes its first successful flight, and is rewarded by its parent with regurgitated prey.*

138 *Although the parent bird has returned from foraging, it does not approach the fledglings. Juvenile little egrets fly from tree to tree vigorously pursuing the parent bird and demanding to be fed. Around this time the nesting colony becomes extremely active (little egret).*

139 *Disgorging indigestible material. By examining such matter, it is possible to guess what the birds have eaten.*

141 *During the rainy season, egrets appear to dislike leaving the roost. They wait for the rain to cease and then dash out to forage.*

142   *A little egret forages in a rice paddy on Amami Island.*

143 *Rain forest at the water's edge (Amami Island).*

Foraging from the early morning on, a fledgling takes flight (great, intermediate, and cattle egrets). According to records, about two thousand little and cattle egrets once flocked in a single colony in the Nara Basin, making a 320-square-meter area their exclusive foraging site.

▶145 *Arrival at the roost at dusk.*

146 *Alighting on the roosting forest.*

▶147 *Leaving the roost at sunset.*

148 *Nightfall at the nesting colony.*

Autumn

As the time nears for the young birds to leave their nests, changes appear in the egret community and in the bodies of the adult birds. The breeding plumage gradually loses its luster and falls out. Head feathers are lost, and bill and lore colors change. When mating ends, both the seminal glands and ovaries shrink, and the birds' body weight drops to facilitate flight. The parent-child bond fades and preparations begin for the approaching winter.

As summer ends, egrets choose a tree or grove nearer their foraging grounds as a roost. Once bustling with activity, the nesting colony gradually becomes desolate as ever-increasing numbers of birds do not return in the evening. Migratory birds part from the flock and move southward. They will travel thousands of miles to the winter retreat at an average speed of thirty-two kilometers per hour, resting on small islands—like Yoron and Amami islands—along the way. Nonmigratory birds scatter to different winter roosts while short distance migratory birds leave for different regions of Japan. At this time, it is possible to witness the breathtaking sight of flocking white egrets heading west across the Kannon Straits at sunset.

Eventually, the entire colony stands hushed and vacant.

149 *Great egret in a field of ripening rice. The mortality rate of young egrets during their first year of life is 75 percent.*

150   *Golden rice fields (little egret). Although the birds instinctively know where to hunt for prey, practice and experience improve their foraging abilities.*

151 *Evening mist over the river's mouth.*

▶152 *Morning fog over rice fields (little egrets).*

153 *Little egret in mid-autumn.*

154 *While foraging in a pond nearby, little egrets occasionally rest among the autumn leaves.*

155 *Little egrets forage in a shallow pond.*

156　*Little egrets wade in a paddy of withered lotus.*

157　*Little egrets in burning fields.*

158   *Ripened persimmons. Depending on the region, the average distance covered by a foraging egret is from 5 to 13 kilometers; the greatest recorded distance is 25.6 kilometers.*

▶159   *Barren trees of late autumn (little egret).*

160 *Sunrise.*

Winter

Following the autumn departure of migratory birds, little egrets, occasionally accompanied by a small number of great and intermediate egrets, scatter to numerous winter roosts. The dispersal of these flocks during winter and the formation of smaller flocks decreases the competition for prey. The roosts are located closer to the foraging grounds so that birds spend less time commuting, thus consuming less energy and extending the hours available for foraging.

When the birds awaken in the dim light of early winter mornings, their long, low cries of *goah* issue forth in unison. They stretch their necks and prepare to head toward the foraging site. Although the birds typically head out before sunrise, on particularly cold mornings they linger in the forest and delay their flight to the foraging site. At the feeding grounds, birds forage individually, in pairs, in small groups, and in flocks. Relaxing and spreading their broad white wings, they rest in sunny areas to conserve body heat.

The position of the sun determines when the birds enter and leave the roost. Returning to the roost when the sky begins to darken, birds gather by twos and threes in a pre-roosting assembly, either in a nearby forest or in the sky above the roost, although the first birds gathering at the preroosting assembly site may appear as early as three in the afternoon while it is still light. When the surrounding area is fairly dark, the egrets all enter the roost together. Any birds that miss the preroosting assembly enter the roost directly. One theory is that the preroosting assembly is a type of "self-management" behavior. When all the birds have gathered, the number of flock members is assessed in some way and if the food supply in the nearby area cannot support them all, some are forced to leave. This theory, however, has never been proven.

Entering the roost, the birds frequently quarrel as they vie for the ideal perch, but in time the roost grows quiet. As spring nears, the days gradually lengthen. Stimulated by increasing sunlight, reproductive hormones begin to trigger changes in the egret's appearance. The lightly soiled winter plumage is gradually replaced by breeding plumage, and the colors of bills and lores begin again to change. Soon, the egrets head for the mating colonies where the migratory birds have already begun gathering and the cycle begins once again.

162 *A cold day (little egret).*

◄161 *Leaving the roost before sunrise.*

163   *Winter day. Little egrets have purportedly crossed the Atlantic Ocean during migrations.*

164 *Little egrets forage in a wintry field. Their hurried movements differ from the quiet elegance of the great and intermediate egret.*

165 *Winter (great egret).*

166 *As the sun sets.*

167 *Field bathed in sunset colors.*

168　*Intermediate egrets roost in winter treetops.*

169 *Preroosting assembly at the water's edge.*

170 *Returning to the roost at nightfall.*

171 *Egrets swarm in the sky above the roosting forest before landing. Each member of the flock is attuned to the movement of the other birds. Anticipating each other's movements, the flock moves in a smoothly coordinated wave.*

172 *Little egrets perch above the roost.*

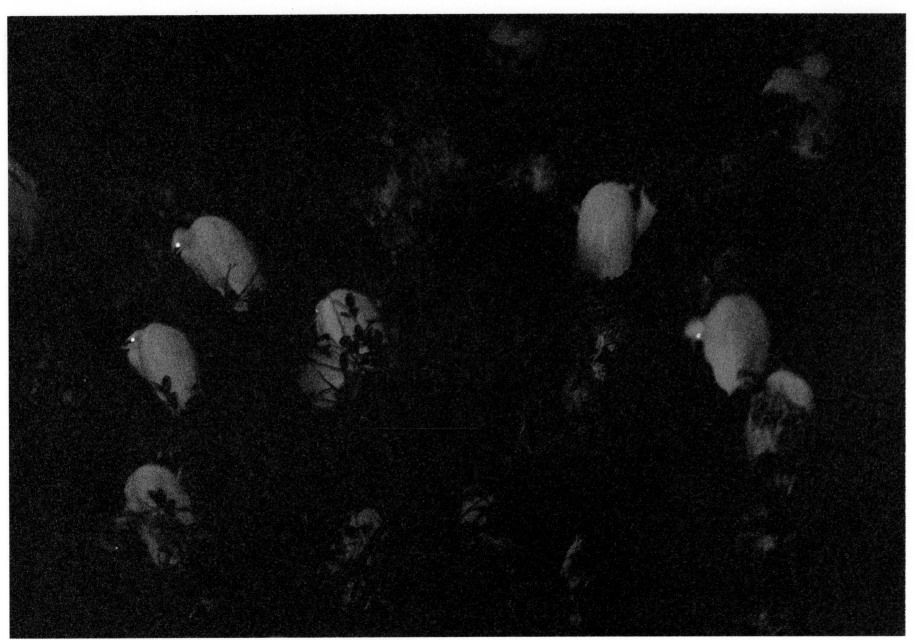

173   *Small quarrels break out as the birds look for their proper roosts, but soon the flock is settled and quiet. Rather than roosting together, the birds prefer to stay several meters apart.*

175 *The roost at midnight.*

176 *Little egrets at a snowy sunrise.*

177 *Harsh winter's morning (little egrets).*

178 *Little egrets in a snowstorm. In winter, little egrets limit the range of their activity to five kilometers, about half of what it is in summer.*

179   *Snowy forest. Birds of the same species tend to occupy the same tree and gather at the same watering holes.*

180 *Deep snow at dusk.*

181 *A clearing in the snow.*

182 *Sunrise over deep snow.*

183   *Snowy flight toward the feeding grounds.*

184   *Snow falling at the water's edge.*

185 *Standing in the snow.*

186 *Great egret.*

187   *Great egret in flight. During flight, the legs extend backwards and protrude from the tail feathers.*

188 *Great egret landing. When landing, the wings beat forward to reduce speed, the body rotates at a right angle to an upright position, and legs stretch forward to absorb the shock of impact.*

189   *Great egret.*

190   *The great egret's average flight speed is about forty kilometers an hour.*

191 *Arrival at the roost.*

▶192 *Flying homeward at sunset.*

193 *Little egret sets off for the roost at dusk.*

194 *Great egret at sunrise.*

195 *Returning to the roost.*